# Collins

# PRIMARY
# WORD WORK

## BOOK 4

Louis Fidge
Sarah Lindsay

Collins Educational

*An imprint of HarperCollinsPublishers*

Published by Collins Educational
An imprint of HarperCollins*Publishers* Ltd
77-85 Fulham Palace Road
London W6 8JB

First published 1998

ISBN 0 00 302489 X

Illustrations by Maggie Brand, Rob Englebright, Belinda Evans, Bethan Matthews, Andrew Midgley, Rhiannon Powell.

British Library Cataloguing in Publication Data
A catalogue record for this book is available from the British Library.

Cover illustration: Belinda Evans
Editor: Janet Swarbrick
Designer: Celia Hart

Printed by Scotprint, Musselburgh

**Acknowledgements**
The authors and publishers wish to thank the following for permission to use copyright material:
Ginny Lapage for 'Word Search' (p.22) and 'Crossword' (p.34) from *Collins Junior Dictionary Workbook*.
Every effort has been made to trace the copyright holders, but if any have been inadvertently overlooked, the publishers will be pleased to make the necessary arrangement at the first opportunity.

# Contents

# UNIT 1

# Our changing language (1)

Many **words** and **expressions** have **changed over a period of time**.

In modern English we would say "Why are you going there?"

Why **goest thou yonder**?

**Verb endings** have changed.

Some words are **no longer used**.

Some words **aren't used much anymore**.

## Practice

Copy these verbs. Join the old version of each verb with the modern version.

| old version | modern version |
|-------------|----------------|
| keepeth | has |
| cometh | are |
| hath | gave |
| shalt | keeps |
| saith | spoke |
| art | comes |
| wilt | shall |
| gavest | should |
| spake | says |
| shouldst | will |

# More to think about

**Match and copy the pairs of sentences.**

**older version**

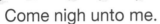
I was anhungered.

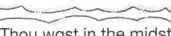
Come nigh unto me.

Thou wast in the midst of the multitude.

He should in no wise be punished.

Where are my brethren?

Who abides in this dwelling?

They ran hither and thither.

**modern version**

Where are my brothers?

Who lives in this house?

I was hungry.

They ran here and there.

You were in the middle of the crowd.

He should definitely not be punished.

Come closer to me.

## Now try these

**Copy these sentences. Write what you think they mean in modern English.**

1. Do what thou art bidden at once!

2. What things soever ye desire, so shall ye have.

3. I tarried awhile, lest my friend appeared.

4. The house was bestowed upon me by my father.

5. The old and infirm remaineth within the building.

6. Verily I say unto thee, thou art wondrous to behold.

# UNIT 2 Unstressed vowels

All words can be divided into **stressed** and **unstressed syllables**.

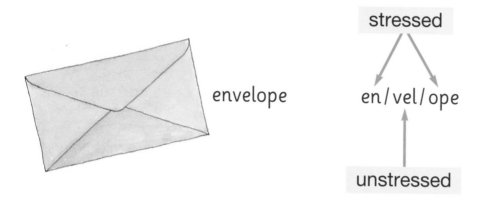

stressed

envelope       en / vel / ope

unstressed

The unstressed syllables may sometimes include a **vowel** that is **hard to hear**. This is called an **unstressed vowel**.

en / v**e**l / ope

## Practice

1. Copy the words. Split each word into its syllables.

   a) interest   in / ter / est

   b) company        c) freedom        d) entrance

   e) diesel         f) valuable       g) history

   h) deodorant      i) extra          j) dictionary

2. In each of the words above, underline the syllables that include the unstressed vowel, like this:

   a) interest   in / <u>ter</u> / est

# More to think about

1. Copy the words. Divide each word into syllables.
   Underline the unstressed syllable in each word.
   
   a) cruel   cru / <u>el</u>
   b) problem
   c) sister
   d) effort
   e) cathedral
   f) available
   g) constable
   h) entrance
   i) travel
   j) button
   k) Wednesday
   l) dungeon

2. Circle the unstressed vowel in each of the words above, like this:

   a) cruel   cru / c(e)l

## Now try these

1. The two words in each pair are in the same word family.
   Copy the pairs and underline the word in each that has
   an unstressed vowel.
   
   a) photograph      photographer
   b) mental          mentality
   c) celebration     celebrity
   d) temperate       temperature

2. Write a pair of words from another word family using
   one word with a stressed vowel and one where the
   same vowel is unstressed.

# Origins of proper names

Many **proper names**, like the names of the days and months, and lots of our towns and villages, have interesting **historical origins**.

The **sun** has always been very important to people, so a day was named after it. **Sunday** got its name from the Latin *solis* (**sun**) *dies* (**day**). This was translated into Old English as *sunnendaeg* (**day** of the **sun**).

## Practice

**Copy the names of the days and match them with their origins.**

| | |
|---|---|
| **Sunday** | This was named after a Viking god of war called Tiwes. It was originally called *Tiwesdaeg*. |
| **Monday** | Saturn was a Roman god. His day was translated into Old English as *Saeternesdaeg*. |
| **Tuesday** | This comes from the Old English word *Sunnesdaeg*, which means day of the sun. |
| **Wednesday** | Thor was the Viking god of thunder. In Old English the day named after him was called *Thursdaeg*. |
| **Thursday** | This day was named after Woden, who was the king of all Viking gods. In Old English it was written as *Wodensdaeg*. |
| **Friday** | This day was named after the moon. It was originally written as *Monandaeg*. |
| **Saturday** | Frigg was a Viking goddess of love. This day was named after her, *Frigesdaeg*. |

# More to think about

**Copy these explanations. After each, write the month or months it describes.**

Did you know that the names of the months all come from the Romans? There were originally only ten months, but two more were specially created for two important Roman Emperors.

1. Maia was the Roman goddess of spring.

2. This month was named after Emperor Augustus.

3. Februa was an important Roman festival.

4. Juno was the main Roman goddess.

5. Janus was a god with two faces.

6. This comes from the Latin word *aprilis*, when buds open.

7. Mars was the the Roman god of war.

8. This month was named in honour of the emperor Julius Caesar.

9. These months are named after the Roman numbers for seven (*septem*), eight (*octo*), nine (*novem*) and ten (*decem*).

## Now try these

The Celts lived in Britain before the Romans. Some place names still have Celtic origins.

1. Match the Celtic words with the town or place names that include them.

> bal = a village
> comb = a valley
> ben (or pen) = a mountain
> lin = a pool
> inver (or aber) = a river mouth
> llan = a sacred place
> strath = a broad valley
> cant = a corner
> dun (or carrick) = a hill

a) Balmoral (bal)  b) Aberdeen  c) Llandaf

d) Canterbury  e) Carrickfergus  f) Ilfracombe

g) Strathaven  h) Ben Nevis  i) Lindale

2. Look at a map of the British Isles. Find one more place name for each Celtic word.

# Prefixes

A **prefix** is added to the beginning of a word to **change** its **meaning**.

He rode his **tri**cycle through the **sub**way.

Remember, when a **prefix** is added to a word it **does not change the spelling** of the root word.

## Practice

1. Copy these words. Underline the prefix in each.

   a) <u>bi</u>cycle      b) teleprinter      c) aquaplane      d) subdivide

   e) biannual      f) aerodynamics      g) incapable      h) triangle

   i) submerge      j) inexperience

2. Choose five words from above and use each one in a different sentence.

Use a dictionary if you need to.

# More to think about

Complete each word with the correct prefix from the box. Use a dictionary to help.

| hydro | sub | in | tri |
|---|---|---|---|

1. _____ appropriate

2. _____ cycle

3. _____ conscious

4. _____ electric

5. _____ angular

6. _____ experience

7. _____ heading

8. _____ foil

## Now try these

1. Copy the words. Write their definitions, using your dictionary to help.

   a) inability    b) inarticulate    c) inaccessible

   d) submerge    e) subway    f) subside

   g) triangle    h) tricolour    i) tripod

2. Underline the prefix in each of the words above. Write what you think the prefix means in each of the three groups of words.

# UNIT 5
# Our changing language (2)

The English language is still **growing** and **changing**.

> Do you like my new **trainers**?

> I can do a **wheelie**!

> How I hate **mobile phones**!

**New words** are needed all the time to describe things like **new skills**, **fashions** and **inventions**.

## Practice

**Copy each word and match it with its definition.**

| | |
|---|---|
| **countdown** | a machine that plays and records video cassettes |
| **trainers** | a hotel where motorists can park close to their rooms |
| **video recorder** | counting downwards before an important beginning |
| **aerosol** | an aircraft that flies using a set of large rotating blades |
| **supersonic** | a long narrow board used for surfing |
| **monorail** | a type of shoe worn for sports or casual wear |
| **helicopter** | something that travels faster than the speed of sound |
| **motel** | a can filled with liquid under pressure |
| **surfboard** | a train that moves on a single rail |

# More to think about

**Copy the table.**
**Write the words in the box**
**in the correct columns.**

Here are some new words that have recently entered our language.

| sneakers | Internet | astronaut | burger |
| floppy disc | jeans | milkshake | parka | microchip |
| | satellite | brunch | launch pad |

| Words to do with: | | | |
|---|---|---|---|
| **clothes** | **food and drink** | **computers** | **space travel** |
| | | | |
| | | | |
| | | | |

# Now try these

1. Think of some new words that end with these suffixes.

   a) **phone** (from the Greek word meaning *a sound*)

   b) **scope** (from the Greek word meaning *I see*)

2. Think of some new words that begin with these prefixes.

   a) **micro** (from the Greek word meaning *very small*)

   b) **tele** (from the Greek word meaning *from afar*)

3. Think of some new words that have
   entered our language to do with:

   a) transport

   b) fashions

   c) electrical goods

# Spelling rules (1)

Remember these rules when adding **suffixes** to most words.

1. In a word where the **last syllable is stressed**, and the <u>letter before last is a single vowel</u>, the **last letter** is normally **doubled**. (But the letters **w**, **x** and **y** are **never doubled**.)

stop          stopping          stopped

2. When a word ends with **y** (making the **ee** sound), the **y** changes to an **i** when the suffix is added.

lonel**y**          lonel**i**ness

3. Only one **l** is used on suffixes ending with **ful**.

help          help**ful**

## Practice

**Copy these words. Write the spelling rule number next to each word.**

1. pain ⟶ painful    Spelling rule 3

2. wonder ⟶ wonderful          3. marry ⟶ marriage

4. nasty ⟶ nastiness          5. drop ⟶ dropping

6. wrap ⟶ wrapper          7. carry ⟶ carried

8. easy ⟶ easily          9. swim ⟶ swimming

# More to think about

1. Copy the words. Write each word without its suffix.

   a) doubtful       b) mysterious       c) married

   d) bossiest       e) wrapped       f) dreadful

   g) beginning       h) chilliest       i) merriment

   j) putting       k) quarrelling       l) masterful

2. Use all the words above in a passage of writing about
   a weekend adventure.

## Now try these

Copy the table. Write each root word with
its suffix in the appropriate column.

| Root word | ful | ing | ness | est |
|-----------|-----|-----|------|-----|
| happy | – | – | happiness | happiest |
| beauty | | | | |
| wrap | | | | |
| spite | | | | |
| busy | | | | |
| program | | | | |
| foggy | | | | |
| thought | | | | |
| deceit | | | | |
| pretty | | | | |
| hungry | | | | |

# Etymology (1)

**Etymology** is the study of **word origins** and **formation**. The English language has been **influenced** by **many other languages**.

This is what a dictionary says about the word **diary**.

> **diary**  1.  a daily record of events or thoughts
> 2.  a book for noting future engagements
> (L. *diarium*)

> In Roman times a *diarium* originally meant a daily allowance of pay. Soon it came to mean the note book in which daily payments were recorded. Later still it came to have its present meaning!

This means it comes from the Latin (L) word *diarium*.

**Dictionaries** often tell us where a word **originates** from.

## Practice

Copy the table. Sort these words, which originate from the Anglo Saxon, into the correct columns.

| cow arrow fish king goose axe oar sail bow |
| knight lord sheep shield ship queen hen |

| Words to do with: | | | |
|---|---|---|---|
| animals | fighting | the sea | important people |
| | | | |

# More to think about

**Copy the sentences. Use a word in the box to fill each gap.**

These words all came into our language from the French after the Norman invasion.

| pardon | burglary | judge | jail |
| crime | constable | debt | court |

Mr Norman got into _____ , so he decided to do a _____ . Unfortunately a _____ caught him. He was taken to _____ . The _____ said that as this was his first _____ he would _____ him. Mr Norman was lucky not to go to _____ .

## Now try these

**Refer to the key and write which language each word came from. Then look up the definition for each word in your dictionary.**

1. banquet (F.)  (French)  A banquet is a large special meal held to celebrate a special occasion.

2. dynamo (Gk.)      3. specimen (L.)      4. algebra (Arab.)

5. concerto (It.)      6. lager (G.)      7. idol (Da.)

8. bamboo (Mal.)      9. turban (Turk.)      10. alligator (Sp.)

11. shamrock (Ir.)      12. buoy (Du.)

---

**Key**

Arab. = Arabic  Da. = Danish  Du. = Dutch  F. = French

G. = German  Gk. = Greek  Ir. = Irish  It. = Italian

L. = Latin  Mal. = Malayan  Sp. = Spanish  Turk. = Turkish

# Mnemonics

A **mnemonic** is a way of remembering the spellings of tricky words. To remember the **lie** in the middle of be**lie**ve think of this sentence.

I haven't picked any flowers

DO NOT PICK THE FLOWERS

Never be**lie**ve a **lie**.

The **mnemonics** that work the best are the ones you make up yourself!

## Practice

**Copy the words. Underline the part or parts of the word the mnemonic is helping with.**

1. advice     Advice is a noun and so is **ice**.

2. where      Where is **here**?

3. government  The government **governs** over society.

4. dictionary  Mary reads the dictionary to improve her **diction**.

5. separate    Separate has **a rat** in it.

6. bicycle     Don't ride your bicycle in **icy** weather.

# More to think about

1. Copy the sentences. Fill the gap with the appropriate word from the box.

| island | ambitious | sword | twelfth | weight | separate |

a) _____ has A RAT in it.

b) The _____ ELF is a TWin.

c) An _____ IS LAND surrounded by water.

d) I AM not a BIT _____.

e) Not a WORD, just SWing the _____.

f) What's the _____ of EIGHT people?

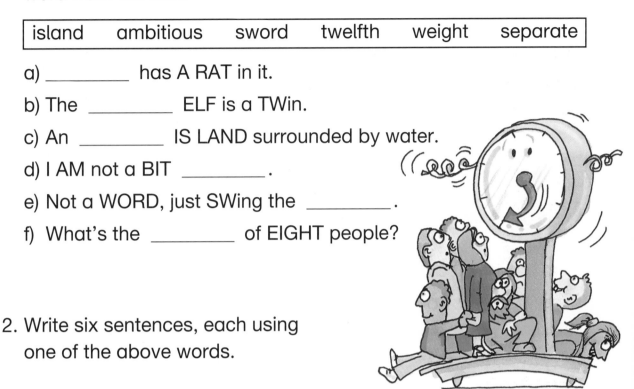

2. Write six sentences, each using one of the above words.

## Now try these

**Write your own mnemonics to help you remember these spellings.**

1. vegetable
2. reel
3. dessert
4. knight
5. teacher

# Proverbs

A **proverb** is a **short, wise saying** which has been in use for **many years**.

As well as its obvious meaning, this also means that people mix with others who have similar tastes and interests to their own.

Look before you leap.

Birds of a feather flock together.

Some proverbs are **easy** to understand.

Some proverbs have **more than one meaning**.

## Practice

**Choose the best word to complete each well-known proverb.**

| another | speed | served | bread | parted |
|---|---|---|---|---|
| | never | alike | clean | |

1. A fool and his money are soon _____ .

2. More haste, less _____ .

3. Half a loaf is better than no _____ .

4. One good turn deserves _____ .

5. First come, first _____ .

6. New brooms sweep _____ .

7. Great minds think _____ .

8. Better late than _____ .

# More to think about

1. Match each proverb to the picture which
   best illustrates its meaning.

   a)

   Every cloud has a silver lining.

   One man's meat is another man's poison.

   Make hay while the sun shines.

   Out of the frying pan into the fire.

   b)            c)            d)

2. Draw a picture which illustrates the meaning of
   "Don't put all your eggs in one basket."

## Now try these

**Copy these proverbs. Write what you think
each one really means.**

1. Too many cooks spoil the broth.

2. A stitch in time saves nine.

3. Practice makes perfect.

4. Still waters run deep.

5. A bird in the hand is worth two in the bush.

6. Let sleeping dogs lie.

7. Two heads are better than one.

8. Courtesy costs nothing.

# UNIT 10 — Spelling rules (2)

Here are some **general rules** that will help you with your spelling.

1. *Spiv* is the only English word that ends in a **v**. No English words end in a **j**.

2. Most words that have a **k** sound <u>after a short vowel sound</u> are spelt with **ck**.

3. The letter **q** is always written with the letter **u** following it.

4. If there is an **ee** or **i** sound at the end of a word it is usually spelt with a **y**.

5. Put **i** (when it makes the sound **ee**) before **e** except after **c**.

ti**ck**
so**ck**

**qu**een
ac**qu**aintance

strawberr**y**
fl**y**

th**ie**ves
c**ei**ling

## Practice

**Copy these words. Write the spelling rule number next to each word.**

1. baby    Spelling rule 4
2. quiet
3. lipstick
4. priest
5. robbery
6. immediately
7. quarrel
8. piece
9. squash
10. squirrel

# More to think about

1. Write the word to match the picture.

a)

j _____

b)

r _____

c)

m _____

d)

s _____

e)

s _____

f)

p _____

g)

r _____

h)

d _____

i)

q _____

2. Write nine sentences, each using one of the words above.

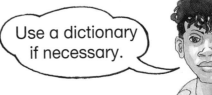

Use a dictionary if necessary.

## Now try these

**Use the clues to help unscramble the letters.**

1. Something that can't be solved:      yeymrts
2. Quite likely:      bbproayl
3. A light hangs from it:      gncilei
4. Tiles are this when they get wet:      rpypelsi
5. Amount:      tuiqtayn
6. Has four sides of equal length:      aqeusr
7. A big feast:      ebntaqu
8. A bag carried behind:      kcbapkac

# Progress Test A

1. Write what you think this means in modern English.

Trespass thou not in yonder field for it hast a bull therein which wouldst chase thee!

2. Copy these words. Split each word into syllables.
   Underline the unstressed syllable, like this: in / <u>ter</u> / est

   a) entrance     b) company     c) problem

   d) mystery     e) envelope

3. a) **septem** (meaning *seven*)

   b) **octo** (meaning *eight*)

   c) **novem** (meaning *nine*)

   d) **decem** (meaning *ten*)

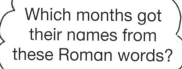

Which months got their names from these Roman words?

4. Choose the correct prefix from the box for each of the words.

   | sub | bi | aero | tele | in |
   |-----|-----|------|------|-----|

   a) _____ dynamic     b) _____ ability     c) _____ cycle

   d) _____ way     e) _____ graph

5. Copy these words. Circle the five words which have most recently come into our language.

   | sneakers | pencil | window | satellite | Internet |
   |----------|--------|--------|-----------|----------|
   | cave | supersonic | village | motel | cup |

6. Copy these words. Write the root word from which each comes.

   a) mysterious    b) politeness    c) beautiful

   d) dropper       e) beginning

7. These words have been borrowed from the French language. Write a definition for each word. Use your dictionary to help.

   | ballet | buffet | antique | cabinet | picturesque |
   |--------|--------|---------|---------|-------------|
   | boutique | grotesque | bayonet | | |

8. Use the words in the box to answer the questions.

   | separate | belief | sword | breakfast | sandwich | vegetables |
   |----------|--------|-------|-----------|----------|------------|

   Which word has:

   a) a **lie** in it        b) **sand** in it        c) a **word** in it

   d) **a rat** in it        e) **break** in it       e) **get** in it?

9. Copy and finish these well-known proverbs.

   a) A stitch in time _____ .

   b) Better late _____ .

   c) One good turn _____ .

   d) Two heads _____ .

   e) Every cloud has _____ .

   f) Too many cooks _____ .

10. Choose **ie** or **ei** to complete each word.

   a) rec ___ ___ pt      b) pr ___ ___ st      c) c ___ ___ ling

   d) p ___ ___ ce        e) bel ___ ___ ve     f) rec ___ ___ ve

# Our changing language (3)

The **meanings** of words can **change** over a period of time.

In the beginning, **box** was used only for the name of a tree (the boxwood tree).

↓

Then the word **box** was used for a container made of boxwood.

↓

Nowadays any container with flat sides may be called a **box**.

Look how the word "box" has changed its meaning.

## Practice

**Copy this table. Write each of these words in the correct place.**

apartment   photograph   great   money   enthusiastic   sell

| Word | An earlier meaning | A more recent meaning |
|------|--------------------|-----------------------|
| wicked | evil | |
| keen | sharp | |
| flog | to beat | |
| snap | break | |
| bread | a food made from flour and water (and often, yeast) | |
| flat | level | |

# More to think about

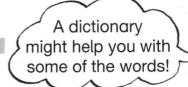

A dictionary might help you with some of the words!

**Copy and complete the table.**

| Word | An earlier meaning | A more recent meaning |
|---|---|---|
| tape | a strip of cloth | |
| hack | | to gain unauthorised access to computer data |
| trainer | a person who trains another | |
| green | | environment-friendly |
| web | | the Internet |

## Now try these

1. Copy these sentences. Write what you think each one means.

a) <u>Deliver</u> me from this evil man.
   Save me from this evil man.

b) What a <u>nice</u> mess you've got yourself in!

c) The green hill was <u>without</u> the city wall.

d) I can <u>fashion</u> a model out of clay.

e) The girl was all sweetness and <u>charity</u> .

2. Now write some sentences of your own. Use each underlined word with its more recent meaning.

# Etymology (2)

Many of the words we use today come from many **different sources**.

Some words are **borrowed from other countries**.

Some words come from the **names of places or people**.

Some words **imitate sounds**.

Some words have **historical origins**.

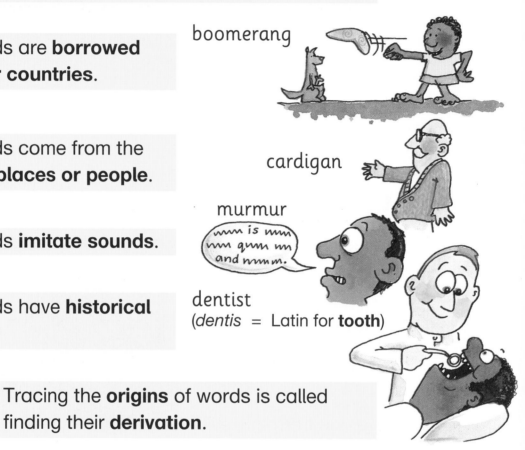

boomerang

cardigan

murmur

~~~ is ~~~
~~~ gum ~~~
and ~~~.

dentist
(*dentis* = Latin for **tooth**)

Tracing the **origins** of words is called finding their **derivation**.

## Practice

**Match each word in Set A with its country of origin in Set B.**

| Set A | curry      | restaurant | kangaroo |
|-------|------------|------------|----------|
|       | yacht      | spaghetti  | wok      |

| Set B | Australia  | France     | China    |
|-------|------------|------------|----------|
|       | Italy      | Holland    | India    |

# More to think about

1. Copy the table. Sort the words in the box into the correct columns.

| splutter wellington yelp knock cuckoo pasteurise hoover sizzle |
|---|

| Words derived from places or people | Words that imitate sounds |
|---|---|
|  |  |
|  |  |

2. Add two more words to each column. Use a dictionary to help.

3. Choose three of the words that derive from places or people. Write a sentence explaining the origin of each word.

## Now try these

1. Copy the words. Link each with its historical origin.

| | |
|---|---|
| autobiography | **beatan** – an Old English word meaning *to beat* |
| sympathy | **auto** – a Greek word meaning *self* |
| battle | **bindan** – an Old English word meaning *to bind* |
| photography | **pathos** – a Greek word meaning *feeling* |
| bandage | **photo** – a Greek word meaning *light* |

2. Think of some more words to link with the historical definitions above.

 Use a dictionary to help.

# Argument words

When we put forward a balanced **argument** there are many words that are helpful to us in **explaining** our **point of view**.

**I believe** that dogs make good pets. **Firstly**, they are good companions. **Furthermore**, the **evidence** suggests that they prevent burglaries. **However**, some people say that dogs are a nuisance, but **in my opinion** they are very easy to look after. **In conclusion**, dogs are good for your health – when you exercise them, you also exercise yourself!

## Practice

**Copy these sentences. Choose the best word from each pair to fill in each gap.**

I think I should have more pocket money.

Here are _____ (surely / several)

reasons to _____ (support / once)

my _____ (next / argument).

_____ (Firstly / Naturally), things are getting more expensive.

_____ (Similarly / Secondly), I need more money as I get older.

_____ (Finally / Different), all my friends get more than me.

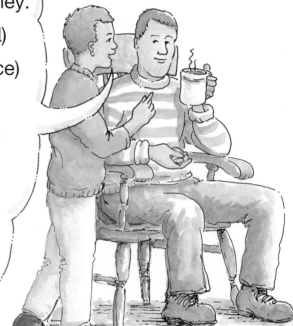

# More to think about

**Copy these sentences.
Choose a suitable word from
the box to fill in the gap.**

Each of the words in this section is a **connective**.

| moreover | furthermore | because | whereas | besides |
| whether | while | during | although | consequently |

I don't think it is fair to have more homework _____ we
already have a lot each night. _____, it is important for
children to have some spare time in the evenings to play. I do
realise that it is necessary to have some homework, like spelling,
_____ for some subjects, like art, I don't think it is
necessary. _____, I don't think every child should have the
same amount of homework, _____ I do think the amount
should increase when children get to secondary school.

## Now try these

| evidence | explanation | alternative | reason | summary |
| opinion | discussion | argument | viewpoint | |
| belief | conclusion | contention | | |

Make up some sentences of your own. Use each of the
words in the box to show you understand its meaning.
Use a dictionary to help if necessary.

# Spelling rules (3)

When adding **suffixes** to most words remember these rules.

1. If the suffix begins with a **vowel** or **y** when the root word ends in **e**, drop the **e**.

   shine      shin**ing**      shin**y**

2. If the root word ends in **ce** or **ge** and the suffix **able** or **ous** is added, keep the **e** .

   replace      replace**able**

3. If you are confused about whether to use the suffix **ible** or **able**, remember <u>many more</u> words use the suffix **able**.

   enjoy      enjoy**able**

## Practice

**Copy these words. Write the spelling rule number next to each word.**

1. drive  ⟶  driving     Spelling rule 1
2. excite  ⟶  exciting
3. value  ⟶  valuable
4. outrage  ⟶  outrageous
5. trace  ⟶  traceable
6. ice  ⟶  icy

# More to think about

1. Choose one suffix from the box to add to each of the words.

| ing | ous | able | ment | ary | ion |
|-----|-----|------|------|-----|-----|

a) imagine     b) place     c) excite     d) develop
e) enjoy       f) leave     g) operate    h) outrage
i) fame        j) invent    k) improve    l) smile

2. Write down the words from above that link with more than one suffix in the box.

3. Write each word from Question 2 with all the suffixes it can end with, like this:

   a) imagine    imagining    imaginary    imaginable

## Now try these

1. Copy the table. Write 15 words that end in the suffix **ible** or **able**. Place them in the correct columns.

| ible | able |
|------|------|
|      |      |
|      |      |
|      |      |

2. Write down which suffix, **able** or **ible**, most of your words end with.

3. Write each word in the table without its suffix, for example: valuable ⟶ value

# Inventing words

In the past, whenever **new** words were needed, they were simply **invented**. These invented words often used **existing words** or **parts of words**.

cheese + hamburger
= cheeseburger

kill-joy
= someone who spoils
things for others

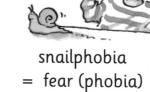

snailphobia
= fear (phobia)
of snails

Sometimes two words were **shortened** into one.

Sometimes **two words were joined together** (often using a hyphen).

If we like we can **invent** new words of our own!

## Practice

**Join and write each word with the two words from which it was made.**

cheeseburger          flutter + hurry

smog                  twist + whirl

twirl                 helicopter + airport

none                  cheese + hamburger

clash                 news + broadcast

flurry                smoke + fog

blurt                 Europe + Asia

slanguage             slang + language

newscast              not + one

Eurasia               blow + spurt

heliport              clap + crash

# More to think about

**Copy the sentences. Choose the most appropriate word to fill each gap.**

1. The king never cared for his subjects. They were very _____ .
2. Another name for a mirror is a _____ .
3. Tom was a cheerful, _____ sort of person.
4. The children had no shoes so they walked _____ .
5. My mum is always cleaning – she's very _____ .
6. The car ran out of petrol and came to a _____ .
7. The camp-site was not neat and tidy but was very _____ .
8. Tim didn't trust the pirate. He looked a real _____ .

rough-and-ready
looking-glass
downtrodden
house-proud
barefoot
cut-throat
standstill
happy-go-lucky

# Now try these

**Have some fun inventing new words of your own.**

1. A **chocaholic** is someone who is addicted to chocolate.
   A **workaholic** is someone who is addicted to work.
   Make up five words of your own with the suffix **aholic**.

2. **Hydrophobia** is a fear of water.
   **Claustrophobia** is a fear of being shut in.
   Make up five words of your own with the suffix **phobia**.

3. Make up some words of your own using these prefixes:
   a) **anti** (meaning *against* as in **anti**septic) such as anti-school!
   b) **ultra** (meaning *extremely* as in **ultra**-modern) such as ultra-brainy!
   c) **poly** (meaning *many* as in **poly**syllabic) such as poly-talented!

# UNIT 16 Root words

These words have the same **root word**.

sun**light**                    **light**house

A **root word** is a word to which **prefixes** or **suffixes** may be added to make other words.

## Practice

**Copy the words. Underline the root word in each.**

1. artistic    <u>art</u>istic

2. subsection

3. bimonthly

4. lonely

5. bicycle

6. export

7. conduct

8. portable

9. telescope

10. inaccurate

11. triangle

12. incomplete

13. annually

# More to think about

1. Join the prefixes and suffixes in the box to the root words.
   Make as many words as you can.

   | ness | ment | ful | auto | bi | al |
   |------|------|-----|------|----|----|

   a) delight      b) right        c) graph

   d) pay          e) together     f) dark

   g) weak         h) monthly      i) mobile

2. Think of two more root words to which each prefix and suffix
   in the box may be added.

## Now try these

1. Copy these root words. Add two more words that use
   the same root word.

   a) smell – smelling, smelly      b) photo        c) love

   d) clear        e) plane        f) help

2. Choose five new root words and add a prefix or suffix.
   Write each of these words in a sentence, for example:
   **cycle**    The <u>cyclist</u> sped up as he saw the finishing line.

# Word games

Playing **word games** can be fun. Word games can help us with **spelling** and can help to **increase our vocabulary**.

Play this word game together. Choose the correct pairs of letters to make the names of some foods. Use a dictionary to help check the spelling.

| gg | tr | ar |
|----|----|----|
| et | rr | tt |
| sy | se | ou |
| ue | sp | zz |

cu _____ y          _____ ifle

g _____ lash      _____ aghetti

ha _____ is       sorb _____

_____ rup          pi _____ a

mering _____      mac _____ oni

omle _____ e      _____ molina

## Practice

**Find the words containing gh in this wordsearch.**
**Write the words in two sets.**

1. In Set 1 write the words in which the **gh** sounds like **f** as in rou**gh**.

2. In Set 2 write the words in which the **gh** is silent as in cau**gh**t.

```
          f s b n c a u g h t g
          d g c r b o c t e o a
          g r m a t o u g h t
        e p l o u g h l g d u
          f d u y p o z h v
      h e d x g j k u w f
      b i y g h z g g v x c e g
      r l k j t b i h a u g h t y y
      f o w y i a y z l x
  i d a u g h t e r h
    o g g g s o p
      h k d j t
      l t h o u g h t q
      m f u u a b r
          w g n
          h x
```

## More to think about

**Copy and complete this puzzle. Use a dictionary to help you.**

1. c a _ _ _ _       a prickly desert plant
2. c l _ _ _       to hold fast to
3. c e _ _ _ _ _       a hundred years
4. c o _ _ _ _ _       to get in touch with
5. c y _ _ _ _       a young swan
6. c r _ _ _ _       to bend low
7. c u _ _ _ _ _ _       a long green salad vegetable
8. c h _ _ _ _ _       a place of worship

## Now try these

Here is a completed crossword. Make up the clues yourself. Use your dictionary to help you.

| ¹G | U | A | ²R | D | I | ³A | N | |
|---|---|---|---|---|---|---|---|---|
| R | | | A | | | H | | ⁴F |
| O | | | N | | | E | | I |
| ⁵V | A | C | C | I | N | A | T | E |
| E | | | I | | | D | | R |
| ⁶L | O | A | D | E | ⁷D | | | Y |
| | | | | | O | | | |
| ⁸P | O | V | E | R | T | Y | | |

# Spelling rules (4)

When making words **plural** remember these rules.

Add **s** to most words.

Add **es** to most words ending in **s**, **x**, **sh** and **ch**.

Drop the last letter and add **ves** to most words ending in **f** or **fe**.

Change the **y** to **i** and add **es** to most words ending in **y** <u>with a consonant before it</u>.

Add **es** to most words that end in an **o** unless it ends in <u>oo</u>, is a music word or is a shortened form.

frog        frog**s**

bush        bush**es**

leaf        lea**ves**

puppy        pupp**ies**

hero        her**oes**

## Practice

**Write the plural for each of these nouns.**

1. turkey
2. photo
3. class
4. country
5. nail
6. piano
7. mosquito
8. lunch
9. glass
10. recipe
11. igloo
12. monkey

# More to think about

**Copy and finish the table.**

| singular | plural |
|---|---|
| gypsy | |
| | elephants |
| | flies |
| daisy | |
| | knives |
| | tattoos |
| | berries |
| sphinx | |
| | dishes |
| bridge | |

## Now try these

**Change each word below to its plural form.
Write a sentence for each pair of words.**

1. library      church
   You can discover many interesting
   things when searching through
   libraries for books on churches.

2. photo        invention
3. baby         nursery
4. cello        glass
5. volcano      thief
6. bus          cuckoo
7. pulley       activity
8. stitch       queen

# UNIT 19 Experimenting with words

English can be exciting because it can offer us so many opportunities to **experiment with words**.

TEAM can be MATE or MEAT or TAME!

I've created a new animal called a catadog!

meeowoof!

Your faces are as red as bowls of tomato soup!

We can **play with words** we like.

We can **create new words**.

We can **create new expressions**.

## Practice

1. Each pet's name is jumbled up. Write each word correctly.

   a) act         b) yonp         c) tarbib         d) semou

2. Make your own jumbled letter words for these pets:

   dog          puppy         kitten         hamster

   fish          budgie        tortoise        gerbil

# More to think about

Make up the names of ten new animals. Use the animal names in the box to help you (or use your own). Draw a picture of the funniest.

> This is a liger.
> It is half lion and half tiger!

| | | | | |
|---|---|---|---|---|
| baboon | camel | cheetah | crocodile | elephant |
| giraffe | gorilla | hyena | kangaroo | lion | monkey |
| ostrich | panda | pelican | penguin | rhinoceros |
| snake | tiger | zebra | hippopotamus |

# Now try these

Complete each sentence to make up an interesting simile of your own.

1. My grandad's beard is like <u>a thick white cotton-wool cloud</u>.
2. The wild wind at night sounds like _____ .
3. The soft sea lapping on the beach is like _____ .
4. The prickles on the hedgehog's back are like _____ .
5. The coward was trembling like _____ .
6. When he came in, his hands were as cold as _____ .
7. When she was chased by the bull, the girl ran as fast as _____ .
8. When Mrs Asif won the Lottery, she was as happy as _____ .
9. The shark zoomed after the diver like _____ .
10. In the morning, the snow covered the ground like _____ .

# UNIT 20 Suffixes

**Suffixes** are added to the end of words.

A **suffix** can change the **tense** of a word.

walk      walk**ed**
(present ⟶ past)

A suffix can change the **class** of a word.

walk      walk**er**
(verb ⟶ noun)

## Practice

1. Copy the table. Write the words in the box in the correct columns.

| boundary | assistant | difference | intelligence |
|----------|-----------|------------|--------------|
| dictionary | ignorant | computer | prisoner |
| explorer | burglary | primary | driver |

| ence | ant | er | ary |
|------|-----|-----|-----|
|  |  |  |  |
|  |  |  |  |

2. Write the root word of each word above.

# More to think about

| ary | ent | ery | hood | ance |
|---|---|---|---|---|

1. Choose a suffix from the box to complete each word.
   Write the word.

   a) neighbour _____     b) differ _____     c) mock _____

   d) assist _____     e) father _____     f) import _____

2. Choose a suffix from the box to add to each root word.
   Write the word.

   a) burgle          b) urge

   c) bribe           d) distant

   e) nurse           f) machine

## Now try these

1. Copy the pairs of words. Write how adding a suffix has
   changed the class of these words.

   a) suggest ⟶ suggestion     verb to noun

   b) magnet ⟶ magnetise

   c) shout ⟶ shouted

   d) quiz ⟶ quizzing

   e) pollute ⟶ pollution

   f) whisper ⟶ whispered

   g) microscope ⟶ microscopic

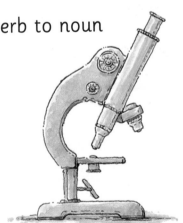

2. Write two sentences for each pair of words above
   showing how the addition of a suffix changes the
   meaning of the word.

# Progress Test B

1. Copy this table. Complete the missing words.

|  | Earlier meaning | Newer meaning |
|---|---|---|
| flat |  | an apartment |
| trainer |  | type of sports shoe |
| green |  | someone who cares for the environment |
| keen |  | enthusiastic |

2. Copy these words. Write the words that come from the names of people.

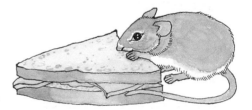

| book | braille | mouse | sandwich | pasteurise |
|---|---|---|---|---|
|  | nail | foot | cardigan |  |

3. Divide these argument words into pairs according to the numbers of syllables they contain.

| while | moreover | whereas | furthermore |
|---|---|---|---|
| opinion | next | surely | notwithstanding |

4. Choose a suffix in the box to add to each word.
   Write the new words you make.

| ous | able | ment | ary | tion |
|---|---|---|---|---|

a) value    b) operate    c) fame    d) outrage    e) govern

5. Write the two words that have been shortened and put together to make each of these words:

a) motel    b) sportscast    c) heliport    d) neither    e) Eurasia

6. Copy these words and write the root word from which each came:

a) excitement    b) graphics        c) inescapable

d) unhelpful      e) happily

7. Write a pair of letters in each gap to make the names of musical instruments.

ce

re        ba

ha        sa        vi

cl        ob        bu

pi        gu

fl

a) _____ute          b) _____corder      c) _____xophone

d) _____llo          e) _____oe          f) _____njo

g) _____arinet       h) _____rp          i) _____olin

j) _____gle          k) _____ccolo       l) _____itar

8. Write the plural form of each word.

a) bush        b) fox        c) boss        d) knife

e) family      f) sheep      g) hero        h) piano

9. Unscramble each anagram to make another word.

a) astute      b) liar

c) bleats      d) battle

e) caned       f) earth

g) horse       h) lamp

10. Choose the correct suffix from the box to add to each of the words. Write the new words you make.

| ary | ery | ant | ent |
|-----|-----|-----|-----|

a) bound       b) assist      c) mock        d) differ

e) preside     f) attend      g) rock        h) diction